For information address Disney Press, 1200 Grand Central Avenue, Glendale, California 91201.

ISBN 978-1-368-03999-4
Printed in China
First Slipcase Edition, August 2018
10 9 8 7 6 5 4 3 2 1

For more Disney Press fun, visit www.disneybooks.com

Disney
Lady and the TRAMP

DISNEP PRESS
Los Angeles • New York

Lady lived very happily with her owners, Darling
and Jim Dear. When Lady grew up, they gave her a
collar with a license. Lady proudly showed her collar to
her friends Jock and Trusty.

"She's a full-grown lady," said Jock.

Tramp was a dog who lived on the streets, living off scraps and helping his friends escape the dogcatcher.

One day, Tramp overheard Lady saying that Jim Dear and Darling were expecting a baby.

"What's a baby?" Lady asked.

"A home-wrecker, that's what," said Tramp.

Lady's happy life was about to change. . . .

When Jim Dear and Darling decided to take a trip, Aunt Sarah came to look after the baby. Her two Siamese cats came, too. Aunt Sarah was not very nice to Lady.

Her two cats were not very nice, either. They made
a mess of the house and pretended that Lady had caused
the trouble.

"Oh, that wicked animal!" said Aunt Sarah.

Aunt Sarah took Lady straight to the pet shop.
"I want a good, strong muzzle," Aunt Sarah said.
The muzzle scared Lady. She jumped off the counter and ran out of the door, not knowing where she was going.

Lady ran and ran. Soon some big, mean dogs
started to chase her. Lady was scared and ran into an
alley. Luckily, Tramp heard all the barking and raced to
Lady's rescue.

"Oh, poor kid," said Tramp, looking at Lady's muzzle. "We've gotta get this thing off. Come on."

Tramp took Lady to the zoo. Maybe one of the animals could help her.

The apes, the alligator, and the hyena were no help at all. Then Lady and Tramp found the beaver. He loved to chew and soon bit right through the muzzle strap!

"It's off!" Lady said with relief.

The beaver was happy, too. He could use the muzzle as a handy-dandy log puller. Lady and Tramp thanked the beaver and left the zoo together.

Then Tramp took Lady to supper at Tony's Restaurant. Tramp's friend Tony liked Lady and fed the pair his specialty—spaghetti and meatballs!

Tramp and Lady accidentally picked up the same piece of spaghetti. The next thing they knew, they were kissing! Lady and Tramp were falling in love. They went to watch the moon rise over the city.

The next morning, on the way home, Lady and Tramp passed a chicken coop.

"Ever chased chickens?" Tramp asked. He couldn't resist.

Lady did not like the idea, but she followed him anyway. The chickens ran around the yard squawking and squealing.

"Hey, what's going on in there?" the farmer called.

Lady and Tramp ran away as fast as they could. But
Tramp soon discovered that Lady wasn't behind him.
She had run into the dogcatcher and been taken to the
dog pound!

Lady was scared to be at the dog pound, but soon the dogcatcher came. Reading her collar, he knew where to take her.

"You're too nice a girl to be in this place," he said, and returned Lady to Aunt Sarah.

At home, Aunt Sarah chained Lady to the doghouse in the garden. Lady was so sad, even Jock and Trusty could not cheer her up.

Then Tramp arrived. Lady was angry with him.
She thought Tramp had only looked out for himself
and had let her get caught.

He tried to explain. "I thought you were right behind me, honest," he said.

"Goodbye. And take this with you," Lady said, returning the bone that Tramp had given her.

Just then, Lady saw a rat creeping into the
baby's room. She couldn't chase it, because of the
chain. She could only bark.

"Stop that!" Aunt Sarah called. "Hush."

But Tramp heard and rushed back to Lady.

"What is it?" Tramp asked.

"A rat in the baby's room!" Lady replied.

Tramp ran into the house and saw the rat. He had
to catch that rat before it hurt the baby.

Meanwhile, Lady was barking with all her might and pulling on the heavy chain. At last the chain broke free from the doghouse. Lady ran inside to help Tramp.

Tramp had chased the rat under the baby's crib and accidentally knocked it over, making the baby cry.

But Lady was happy because the baby was safe— Tramp had finally caught the rat.

Aunt Sarah was not happy, however. The baby's
crying had woken her up, and she had found Lady and
Tramp in his room. She thought they were hurting the
baby. She called the dogcatcher to come for Tramp.

The dogcatcher soon arrived and put Tramp in his wagon. Just then, Jim Dear and Darling came home. Lady tried to explain what had happened. She lifted the curtain to show that Tramp had caught the rat and saved the baby.

Jock and Trusty had a plan to stop the dogcatcher's wagon. They barked loudly, scaring the horses. The wagon crashed, and Tramp was saved.

Jim Dear and Lady found him and took him back to their home.

The next Christmas Eve, Jock and Trusty came by to see Lady, Tramp—and their four new puppies!

"They've got their mother's eyes," said Trusty.

"There's a bit of their father in them, too," said Jock, watching a mischievous little gray puppy.

Everyone was happy that Tramp had become part of the family.